B

JUST-RIGHT
leveled readers

Night on the Farm
An Animal Friends Reader

by **Liza Charlesworth**
illustrated by **Ian Smith**

Text copyright © 2015 by Liza Charlesworth
Illustrations copyright © 2015 Scholastic Inc.

ISBN: 978-0-545-85964-6

10 9 8 7 6 5 4 3   15 16 17 18 19/0

Printed in the U.S.A.   40
First printing 2015

Book design by Maria Mercado

P9-DGI-659

SCHOLASTIC INC.

It is night on the farm.

Time to eat your dinner.

It is night on the farm.

Time to take your bath.

It is night on the farm.

Time to brush your teeth.

It is night on the farm.

Time to put on your pj's.

It is night on the farm.

Time to read your book.

It is night on the farm.

Good night!

Time to say good night!

It is night on the farm.

Time to put out the light.

Comprehension Boosters

1. What animals live on this farm? Which is your favorite?

2. What do the farm animals do at night that you do, too?

3. What is your favorite thing to do at night? Talk about it.